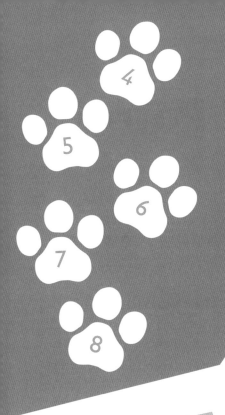

LEFT, RIGHT, UP, DOWN
Activity Book

Colour the paw print when you complete a page. See how far you've come!

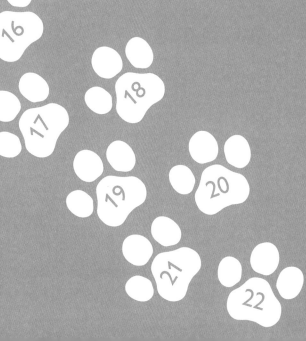

Author:
Carole Asquith

How to use this PAW Patrol Activity Book

This PAW Patrol Left, Right, Up, Down Activity Book has been written to provide an introduction to position and direction words. Fun activities with the PAW Patrol will help your child to learn and understand the concepts of position and direction. The range of activities will help them to recognise and describe relationships between different objects using a range of positional language and prepositions.

- Find a quiet, comfortable place to work.
- This book has been written in a logical order, so start at the first page and help your child to work their way through.
- Read out the instructions to your child where necessary and make sure that they know what to do.
- End each activity before your child gets tired in order to ensure that they will be keen to return to the activities next time.
- Help and encourage your child to check their own answers as they complete each activity. (Answers can be found on page 24.)
- Let your child return to their favourite pages after they have completed them. Talk about the activities they enjoyed and what they have learnt.
- Remember to give plenty of praise and encouragement.
- Once your child has completed all the activities in the book, reward them for their effort and achievement with the certificate on page 23.

Let the PAW Patrol help you with Left, Right, Up, Down!

PAW Patrol – here to help!

ACKNOWLEDGEMENTS

Published by Collins
An imprint of HarperCollins*Publishers* Ltd
The News Building, 1 London Bridge Street, London SE1 9GF

HarperCollins*Publisher*
Macken House, 39/40 Mayor Street Upper, Dublin 1, D01 C9W8, Ireland

© HarperCollinsPublishers Ltd 2023

10 9 8 7 6 5 4 3

ISBN 978-0-00-862005-9

The author asserts the moral right to be identified as the author of this work. All rights reserved. No part of this publication may be reproduced, stored in a retrieval system, or transmitted, in any form or by any means, electronic, mechanical, photocopying, recording or otherwise, without the prior permission of Collins.

British Library Cataloguing in Publication Data

A Catalogue record for this publication is available from the British Library.

©2023 Spin Master Ltd. PAW PATROL and all related titles, logos, characters; and SPIN MASTER logo are trademarks of Spin Master Ltd. Used under license. Nickelodeon and all related titles and logos are trademarks of Viacom International Inc.

Author: Carole Asquith
Publisher: Jennifer Hall
Project editor: Katie Galloway
Cover design: Sarah Duxbury
Internal design: Ian Wrigley
Layout: Rose & Thorn Creative Services Ltd
Production: Emma Wood
Printed in India by Multivista Global Pvt. Ltd.

Contents

Left and right

Which frog is on the **left**? Colour it green.

Which rabbit is on the **right**? Colour it purple.

Which fish is on the **left**? Colour it orange.

Circle the correct word to finish each sentence.

The bee is on the **left / right**.

The butterfly is on the **left / right**.

The ladybird is on the **left / right**.

Rubble is showing the pups where to park their pup vehicles.

Help him by putting a circle around the arrow that points to the **right**.

Cap'n Turbot is trying to work out which way to sail his boat.

Help him by putting a circle around all the arrows that point to the **left**.

Up and down

Which pups are **up** the ladder? Tick the right answers.

Zuma

Rubble

Skye

Colour the animal that is **up** the tree.

The pups are having fun on the hill. Put a circle around the pups that have come **down** the hill.

Follow the directions to show Farmer Yumi where to find the box of vegetables.

Trace the route with your pencil.

Move **up** 3 arrows.

Move **right** 3 arrows.

Move **down** 2 arrows.

Move **left** 1 arrow.

Move **down** 1 arrow.

Move **right** 4 arrows.

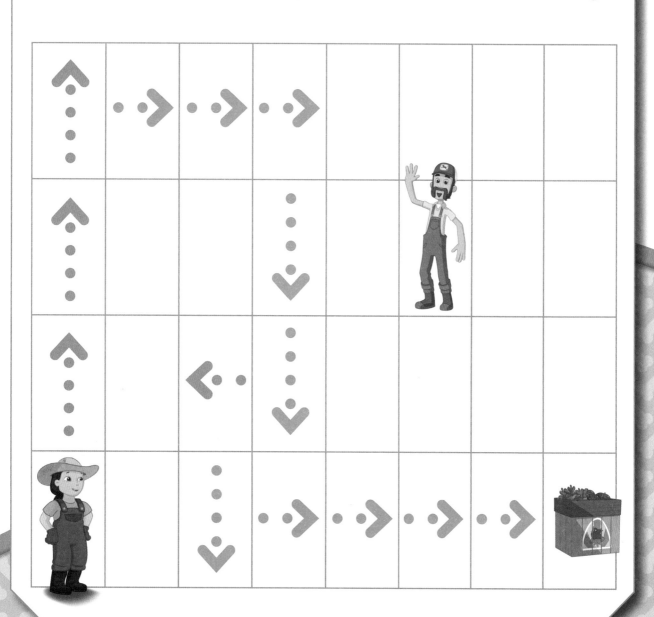

Forwards and backwards

Which pups are facing **forwards**?
Tick the right boxes.

Which pups are facing **backwards**?
Put a circle around them.

Colour the pups that are looking **forwards**.
Put a circle around the pups that are looking **backwards**.

Tick the correct answers to finish the sentences.

If Rocky goes **forwards**, he will find a…
book ☐ **truck** ☐

If Chase goes **backwards**, he will find a…
ball ☐ **camera** ☐

If Marshall goes **forwards**, he will find a…
drum ☐ **keyboard** ☐

Above and below

Colour the stars yellow that are **above** the moon.

Look at the picture.

What is **above** the bridge? Put a tick next to the correct answer.

sun ◯   Rubble ◯   seagull ◯

What is **below** the bridge? Put a tick next to the correct answer.

cloud ◯   boat ◯   tree ◯

On (top of) and under

Look at the picture. Tick the correct sentence.

The frogs are sitting **on top of** the logs.

The frogs are sitting **under** the logs.

Look at the picture. Circle the correct word(s) to finish the sentence.

Rubble and Skye are **under / on top of** the umbrella.

Put a circle around the pup that is **on** the chair. Put a cross on the pup **under** the chair.

Inside and outside

The pups are playing **inside** and **outside** their houses.

Circle the pictures that show pups playing **outside** their houses.

Main Street is busy with traffic and people today.

Who is **inside** the cars? Put a tick next to the correct people.

Who is **outside** the cars? Put a tick next to the correct people.

In and out

Marshall is taking some penguins for a sleigh ride.

Count how many penguins are **in** the sleigh.
Write the number in the circle.

Mr Porter has a box of lemons.

Count how many lemons
are **out** of the box.
Write the number
in the circle.

Ryder has put some toys away in the toy box
but some have been left out.

Count the toys that are still **out** of the box.
Write the number in the circle.

Spot the difference

Look at the pictures. Can you find **3** differences between them? Try to use the position and direction words you have learnt to describe the differences. Put a circle around the differences.

Look at the pictures. Can you find **4** differences between them? Try to use the position and direction words you have learnt to describe the differences. Put a circle around the differences.

Front and back

Look at the line of pups.
Who is at the **front** of the line? Put a tick in the box next to the pup at the front.

The train is leaving for Adventure Bay soon.
There are lots of people waiting to get on board.

Put a tick in the box to show who is at the **back** of the queue.

In front and behind

Colour the butterflies that are **in front** of the tree in the Lookout garden.

Tick the boxes to say whether each pup is **in front** of or **behind** the Lookout.

	In front	Behind
Chase		
Marshall		
Rubble		
Skye		
Rocky		
Zuma		
Everest		

17

Beside and between

Is the ice cream **between** the burgers or **beside** the burgers? Tick the correct box.

between ☐

beside ☐

Is the frog **between** the lily pads or **beside** the lily pads? Tick the correct box.

between ☐

beside ☐

Is the kite **between** the clouds or **beside** the clouds? Circle the correct word.

between

beside

Near and far

Colour the drum that is **near** the toy box.

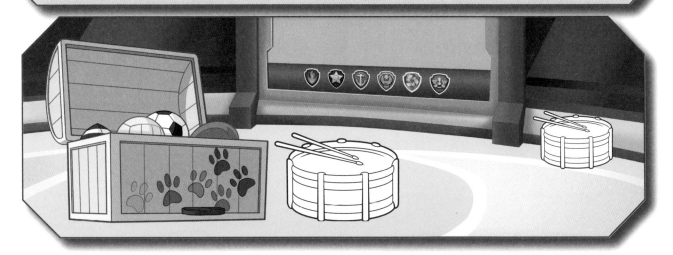

Colour the boat that is **near** to Seal Island.

Put a circle around the 3 hens that are **far** from the squirrel.

Position games

Draw 3 apples **in** the basket. Draw 2 apples **out of** the basket. Colour them red.

Draw a candle **on top of** the cake and colour it.

Draw 2 pup biscuits **beside** each pup bowl and colour them in.

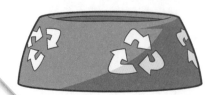

Direction games

Ryder and Rubble are trying to get a lost turtle safely back to the sea. Follow the directions to help them. Trace the route with your pencil, starting at the turtle.

Move **left** 2 arrows.

Move **up** 3 arrows.

Move **left** 3 arrows.

Move **down** 4 arrows.

Move **left** 1 arrow.

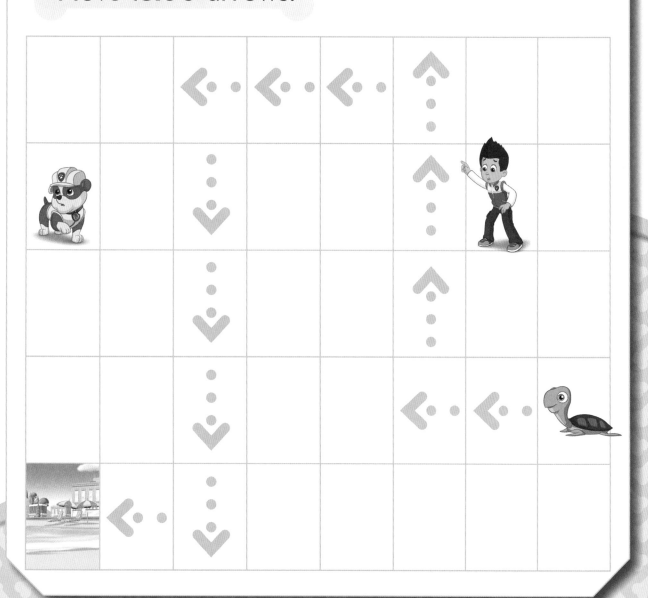

Matching games

Draw a line to match each sentence to the correct picture.

Rocky is **outside** the tent.

The pie is **on** the plate.

Everest is **between** the trees.

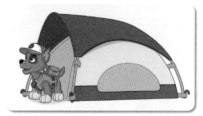

Ryder is **up** the ladder.

The bird is **in** the nest.

Zuma is **under** his blanket.

This badge is awarded to

....

Age ....

For successfully completing

PAW Patrol
Left, Right, Up, Down
Activity Book

Date ....

Signed ....

Well done!

Answers

Page 4
Frog on the left coloured green
Rabbit on the right coloured purple
Fish on the left coloured orange
right circled   **left** circled   **right** circled

Page 5
Arrow pointing to the right circled
3 arrows pointing to the left circled

Page 6
Zuma ✓   Skye ✓
Cali cat coloured
Everest and Chase circled

Page 7

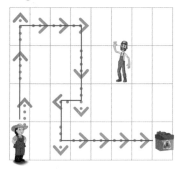

Page 8
Zuma ✓   Rubble ✓   Chase ✓
Rubble and Chase circled

Page 9
Everest, Skye and Rubble coloured; Rocky and Tracker circled
book ✓   camera ✓   keyboard ✓

Page 10
2 stars above the moon coloured yellow
seagull ✓   boat ✓

Page 11
The frogs are sitting on top of the logs. ✓
under circled
Zuma circled; Chase crossed

Page 12
Rubble and Rocky circled

Page 13
5   2   3

Page 14
Bird **in** the sky **above** Liberty in bottom picture; apple **under** the tree in bottom picture; rabbit facing **left** in bottom picture.

Page 15
Shell **under** the parasol in bottom picture; seagull **in** the sky/**above** Chase in bottom picture; Skye facing **right** in bottom picture; frisbee **above** Chase's head in bottom picture.

Page 16
Chase ✓   Mayor Goodway ✓

Page 17
2 butterflies in front of the tree coloured

	In front	Behind
Chase		✓
Marshall		✓
Rubble	✓	
Skye		✓
Rocky	✓	
Zuma	✓	
Everest		✓

Page 18
between ✓   beside ✓   between

Page 19
Drum near the toy box coloured
Boat near Seal Island coloured
3 hens away from the squirrel circled

Page 20
3 apples drawn in the basket and 2 apples drawn out of the basket and coloured red
A candle on top of the cake drawn and coloured
2 pup biscuits beside each bowl drawn and coloured

Page 21

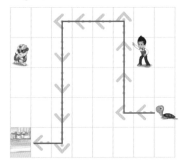

Page 22

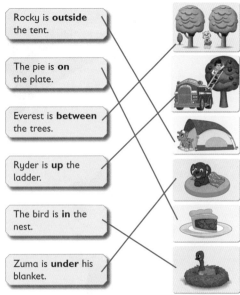

Rocky is **outside** the tent.
The pie is **on** the plate.
Everest is **between** the trees.
Ryder is **up** the ladder.
The bird is **in** the nest.
Zuma is **under** his blanket.

11+
English
Creative Writing

WORKBOOK **2**

Stephen C. Curran

Edited by Andrea Richardson and Warren Vokes

Sub-editor: Katrina MacKay

This book belongs to

Accelerated Education Publications Ltd.

Contents

Chapter Three
The Five Elements of Story

The **Five Elements** of story writing comprise five questions that must be asked about every story that is written. Asking these five questions about your story will help flesh out the details and give you important information to work from before you even start writing.

Where? • When? • Who? • What? • Why?

1. Where Does your Story Happen?
a. The Location of your Story

This refers to your story **Location**. Significant details can be woven into your story to give it a sense of place.

Being specific about where a story occurs can lead you to ask six questions. These six questions will help you pinpoint an exact Location for your story.

We can start with the macro-Location (the country - the biggest possible space) and reduce it right down to the micro-Location (the specific Location of your main Character - the smallest possible space) in which the story takes place.

1. In which **Country**?
2. In what **Region** or **District**?
3. In what **Town** or **Place**?
4. In what **Neighbourhood**, **Vicinity** or **Locality**?
5. In what **Building**, **Street** or **Specific Location**?
6. In what **Room**, **Confined Area** or **Small Space**?

Example 1: Use the six Location questions to pinpoint an exact Location in a story about Mount Everest.

The six questions allow us to pinpoint the exact Location.
1. Country? **Tibet**
2. Region, District or Province? **The Himalayas**
3. Town or Place? **Mount Everest**
4. Neighbourhood, Vicinity or Locality? **Near the summit**
5. Building, Street or Specific Location? **On a narrow ledge**
6. Room, Confined Area or Small Space? **In a small crevice**

Example 2: Use the six Location questions to pinpoint an exact Location in a story set in West Scotland.

1. Country? **United Kingdom**
2. Region, District or Province? **West Scotland**
3. Town or Place? **Glasgow**
4. Neighbourhood, Vicinity or Locality? **Main high street**
5. Building, Street or Specific Location? **Large toy store**
6. Room, Confined Area or Small Space? **Cashier counter**

Exercise 3: 1

Think of a Location you know well and use this method to pinpoint it exactly.

1. Country? ....
2. Region, District or Province? ....
3. Town or Place? ....
4. Neighbourhood, Vicinity or Locality? ....
5. Building, Street or Specific Location? ....
6. Room, Confined Area or Small Space? ....

b. Linking a Location to Story Content

Once you have pinpointed the Location, some of these details can be woven into your story. Avoid 'on the nose' details e.g. 'This story takes place in' etc. This is dull and boring. Try to make your Location details add interest and meaning to the story.

Add Location details to *'The Christmas Lights'* story to lend more meaning to the Story Line.

We could weave some of the details of the Scottish Location into our *'The Christmas Lights'* story by suggesting it is taking place in Scotland without stating it directly or being obvious. The information about Location can contain details which are significant to the meaning and the development of the story. These details are highlighted in bold type.

'Angie stood on the corner of the **busy high street** holding her father's hand. He always **wore his kilt** on special occasions, even if he was freezing cold. **Glasgow winters** were always harsh, but the icy chill seemed to pass right through Angie. 'Oh Little Town of Bethlehem' blared from a nearby speaker outside the **largest toy store in town**.

Angie shivered and glanced back through the glass doors where she could see the **cashier at her counter**. She bit back the tears. Angie was still thinking about how amused the cashier seemed to be when she told her that Father Christmas had gone home for tea and he could not see her today. Shoppers with bright expectant faces, laden with last minute shopping of every kind, dashed by.

Angie stared up above her. The dazzling rainbow haze of lights glowed through the falling snow. Angie had never been to **this part of Glasgow** before. **The poor district of the city** she came from had no pretty Christmas lights.'

c. Describing Locations

One way of stimulating ideas for Description is to write one **significant descriptive statement** against every one of your six Locations to help develop a sense of place and Location. These Descriptions can then be used in your story.

Example: Using the Mount Everest example, write a descriptive statement against each Specific Location.

1. **Country - Tibet**

'As we drove though the ancient villages of Tibet, people everywhere came out of their houses to greet us.'

2. **Region, District** or **Province - The Himalayas**

'As I caught my first view of the Himalayas, their spectacular beauty almost took my breath away.'

3. **Town** or **Place - Mount Everest**

'We knew it would be difficult, but only climbing the highest mountain would satisfy our thirst for adventure.'

4. **Neighbourhood, Vicinity** or **Locality - Near the summit**

'Our breathing became more shallow as we ascended. Every step became more difficult as we neared the summit.'

5. **Building, Street** or **Specific Location - On a narrow ledge**

'We huddled together, exhausted, on the narrow ledge.'

6. **Room, Confined Area** or **Small Space - In a small crevice**

'A small crevice shielded us from the snow and biting wind.'

Exercise 3: 2

Think about the place you chose earlier. Write one statement against every part of this Location.

1. Country

....

....

2. Region, District or Province

....

....

3. Town or Place

....

....

4. Neighbourhood, Vicinity or Locality

....

....

5. Building, Street or Specific Location

....

....

6. Room, Confined Area or Small Space

....

....

d. Active Description

It is essential to use **Active** rather than **Passive Descriptions** when describing Locations otherwise they can seem lifeless and dull. This involves creating moving rather than static images.

Example:  Using the *'Secret Places'* story, demonstrate the use of Active rather than Passive Description.

In our *'Secret Places'* story, the Hero Character stands on the cliff looking out to sea. A quick comparison between Active and Passive Description will illustrate the difference. Try to avoid Passive Description - an example of this might be: *'I looked out to sea. The horizon was visible. It was a clear, sunny day and the sea was a deep blue colour.'*
If we use Active Description this statement will have more life and movement. *'The sunlight shimmered on the sapphire blue sea and I could see for miles: as far as the horizon.'*

Active Description focuses on Movement and Passive Description tends to be static and lifeless. This Movement can be seen from the very first part of the description. We are confronted with moving images from the very start.

'*I struggled up the steep rocky path until I reached my secret place. As I stood on the edge of the cliff, the biting cold wind almost blew me off my feet. My toes tingled with the cold and I shuddered as I gazed out to sea. The fading light from the last of the winter sun shimmered on the sapphire blue water. I squinted my eyes. I could see for miles, even as far as the horizon.*'

Exercise 3: 3

These Storylines lend themselves to Active Location Description. Try writing the opening for one of these stories.

• a girl or boy who cannot swim, who falls into a river
• a police officer who is first on the scene of a car crash
• a fire officer rescuing a child from a burning building

....

....

....

....

....

....

....

....

....

2. When does your Story Happen?
a. Relevant Time Details

This refers to the Time Frame of your story. We must include some details about when a story happened. It is possible to create a hierarchy of Time going from the macro-Time to the micro-Time in a similar way to Location.

1. In which **Century**?
2. In which **Decade**?
3. In which **Year**?
4. In which **Month**?
5. In which **Week**?
6. In which **Day**?
7. In which **Hour**?
8. In which **Minute**?
9. In which **Second**?

If it is important to know about the historical context, or to set the story in a particular period in the Past or the Future, we might need the century, decade or even a specific date.

However, we do not need all this detail for our story to work. Most stories are written about the 'here and now', so we add **Relevant Time Details** to give an idea of the Time Frame.

More general statements about Time can add significant detail to your story. This means it must enhance the meaning of your story in some way. There is a whole batch of **General Time Statements** that can be used.

Time References
Examples might include:
Yesterday; today; tomorrow; next week; last month; a year ago; in about an hour; just this minute; wait a second etc.

Time of Day
Examples might include:
Dawn; morning; afternoon; night; early hours; midday etc.

Time of Year
The use of **seasons** can be very atmospheric as they can act as a metaphor for the cycle of human life.

Spring - birth, infancy, new life, growth, energy and vitality
Summer - fully developed, at the height of physical power
Autumn - maturity and experience, waning physical power
Winter - wisdom, knowledge, physical weakness and death

Festival Occasions

Examples might include:

Christmas; New Year's Day; Harvest Festival; November 5th etc.

Personal Times

These are Times which are significant in a person's life.
Examples might include:

Birthday; anniversary; first day at school; Prize-giving Day etc.

Example:  | Start a story called ***'The Magic Key'*** which includes relevant General Time Statements.

*'**Hannah had always enjoyed birthdays; well until this one.** A few moments before, she had stood motionless, but very excited, before a large cake with exactly **thirteen candles** on it. She had slowly unwrapped the only gift in front of her with great anticipation. A knowing smile crept across her face as each layer peeled away, leaving at last a small box.*

*Hannah couldn't sleep the **night before**. She thought she had already worked out what Mum would buy her. There was the new dress she had pointed out in that designer shop **last week**. Mum had rolled her eyes at the price but she did say she would think about it. Hannah thought it was as good as bought. Her best friend Josie always had the latest designer clothes and Hannah imagined herself just for once being better dressed and more 'cool'. That would teach Josie!*

Hannah would never forget that sinking feeling, a feeling you get when you try to look grateful but you are not. It was just a key; a plain looking door key. She held it up and then looked inside the wrapping for something else. Her friend Josie had looked smug in her new dress.

Astonishingly, Hannah's mum looked pleased with herself. She mumbled something about it opening something important, but Hannah could only feel the anger rising within her. **After all you don't become a teenager every day.** *What was wrong with her mother? Could she not see this would be the biggest joke ever? Josie would never keep it a secret.* **It was the first day back after the holidays, so the whole school would know by tomorrow.**

Hannah cried herself to sleep that night *but as she slept, the key had begun to glow by her bedside.'*

Time Statements are usually indirect. We have included the following information:
• It is Hannah's thirteenth birthday.
• Hannah is becoming a teenager and this is a significant milestone in her life.
• Tomorrow will be the first day back at school.
• There is some information about the week before.
• The actions all take place on one day.

Exercise 3: 4 Think about *'The Dark Forest'* story again. Continue writing from the story opener in Present Tense. Include more Specific Details about Time.

'The trees seem to close in on me. I edge forward. Branches appear to reach out and grab me. There is no way out. Where is the path?

I squint, but can only just see the watch face. Nine o'clock and it is nearly dark. I left three hours ago.

Father had warned me never to go into the forest because of what happened there three years ago. What did he mean?'

....

....

....

....

....

....

....

....

....

....

....

....

b. Time Span

It is effective to set your story within a specific **Time Span**. All stories are highly selective and only show action and scenes relevant to the story. Most stories are confined to hours, days or weeks. Setting a specific Time Limit for the story is called a **Time-lock**. The story now has a fixed end point. This starts a **Ticking Clock** feeling as the story builds to climax.

Example:

Demonstrate the Time-lock and Ticking Clock principle in *'The Tunnel'* story.

We can build in a Time-lock to *'The Tunnel'* story by providing a definite consequence of being caught. We then feel the Ticking Clock sensation as we move to climax. We now find out the main Character's name is Benjy.

'Their threats were still ringing in my ears as I escaped into the tunnel. The balding one with the deep voice said my millionaire daddy would pay a huge sum for his spoilt little brat. But Dave, that's what they all called him, didn't know one of his gang, the one with a limp they called Hoppity, would take pity on me and only tie the rope loosely. They had knives and my one chance to live had come. There must be a way out or I'm dead! Then I heard them screaming abuse. It echoed right through every chamber in the tunnel.

Then Dave's shrill voice, 'Benjy, we're coming to get you.'

As I ran faster, I could see there was a bend in the tunnel up ahead. I could hear footsteps coming from somewhere in the tunnel system. They were getting louder and I could now discern voices. They would kill me if they found me. I gasped heavily and sweat poured down my face. The air was so thin. Just as I reached a bend in the tunnel, my torch suddenly dimmed. I knew the battery was nearly out. Then, to my horror, I found myself in a low, cavern-like space. There were five different tunnels leading off it. The sound of men approaching was now deafening, but coming from which tunnel? I had no idea. The torch flickered and it suddenly went black. Terror gripped me as the sound of footsteps drew closer. The thud of my beating heart crashed into my ears. Which tunnel? Was I in the wrong part of the cavern? I felt completely helpless. I wanted to scream!'

Exercise 3: 5

Continue writing the story **'Inferno'** from this story opener. 'A fire officer tries to rescue a child from a burning building.' The child will die if the fire officer does not act. This is a Time-lock. As the story opens the Ticking Clock starts.

'The flames leapt up the side of the building. Jim was scared. He had only been on shift since midnight. The screams were getting louder. He could see a fair-haired child at the window. The seconds were ticking by. He must act quickly!'

....

....

....

....

....

....

....

....

....

....

....

....

....

3. Who is Involved in the Story?
a. The Main Characters

A successful story must have some interesting and realistic Characters in it. The three most important Characters are:

The Hero (Protagonist) - The central and most important Character in a story. The story is about this Character and what this Character wants to achieve drives the action.

The Opponent (Antagonist) - The second most important Character in the story. The Opponent Character strongly opposes the Hero Character and stands in the way of him or her achieving their aim.

The Sidekick or Ally (Reflection) - This Character is a close supporter of the Hero Character. This Character supports, shares and reflects the aim of the Hero Character. The Sidekick also challenges the Hero Character to change.

Other Characters - These can include:

Wisdom Character - A Character who gives instruction and advice to the Hero Character to help them fulfil their aim.

Sceptic Character - A Character who doubts the Hero Character's abilities and says the aim cannot be achieved.

b. The Three Aspects of Character

All Characters have three aspects:

1. Physical Characteristics (how they look). These include: gender, age, height, build, features, colouring, clothing, skills.

2. Social Characteristics (how they relate to others). These include: quality of relationships with others (good or bad), attitudes to others and how they are viewed by others.

3. Psychological Characteristics (how they think). This is how the Character views him or her self or their mind-set.

Negative traits - timid, frightened, boastful, callous, ruthless.

Positive traits - kind, caring, determined, loving, thoughtful.

Significant Past Event - (painful) e.g. bullied at school.

We can create full Character Profiles for the Characters Billy (Hero), Miss Dagon (Opponent) and Coco (Sidekick).

Hero Character: Name - Billy

Physical Characteristics:

Gender: male **Age:** 8 yrs **Height:** 4 feet **Build:** slender
Features: (Hair) - mousy brown (Face) - freckles, pale complexion (Eyes) - blue **Clothing:** his clothes do not fit.
Skills/Interests: no good at sports **Occupation:** schoolboy

Social Characteristics:

Relationships with others: Billy is a loner with no friends.
Attitude to others: He is scared of bigger boys in his class.
Viewed by others: He is left out and ignored by others.

Psychological Characteristics:

Positive Traits: Billy is determined and cares about others.
Negative Traits: Billy is timid and shy with little confidence.
Significant Past Event: Death of parents.
Beliefs and Attitudes: Billy trusts people.

Opponent Character: Name - Miss Dagon

Physical Characteristics:

Gender: Female **Age:** 55 yrs **Height:** 6 feet **Build:** stout
Features: (Hair) - greying (Face) - chubby, big features (Eyes) - brown, cold **Clothing:** formal, skirt and jacket
Skills/Interests: gardening **Occupation:** house mistress

Social Characteristics:

Relationships with others: No friends and no close relatives.
Attitude to others: Enjoys power and making others suffer.
Viewed by others: Disliked and seen as cruel and uncaring.

Psychological Characteristics:
Positive Traits: Efficient and organised.
Negative Traits: Rigid, not warm or caring.
Significant Past Event: Rejected by her husband and child.
Beliefs and Attitudes: She believes in discipline and control.

Sidekick Or Reflection Character: Name - Coco

Physical Characteristics:

Gender: male **Age:** 50 yrs **Height:** 5 feet 6 inches
Build: thick set **Features** (as a clown): (Hair) - stuck up
(Face) - white, red nose (Eyes) - green **Clothing:** blue
and white striped costume **Skills/Interests:** pratfalls, comic
timing, juggling **Occupation:** clown; grew up in circus.

Social Characteristics:

Relationships with others: The other clowns have begun to
shun him after a few mistakes. They think he is past it.
Attitude to others: He feels threatened by younger clowns.
Viewed by others: Other clowns are jealous because up till
now he has always been the children's favourite clown.

Psychological Characteristics:

Positive Traits: Coco is kind and loving.
Negative Traits: Coco gets depressed and drinks heavily.
Significant Past Event: His wife left him and took the child.
Beliefs and Attitudes: He believes he is unlucky in life.

Exercise 3: 6 Think about *'The Dark Forest'* story
again. An Opponent Character has now
been added. Fill out details on the three
aspects of the Hero and Opponent.

*'The trees seem to close in on me. I edge forward. Branches appear
to reach out and grab me. There is no way out. Where is the path?*

I squint, but can only just see the watch face. Nine o'clock and it is nearly dark. I left three hours ago.

Father had warned me never to go into the forest because of what happened there three years ago. What did he mean? **All he would say was a mysterious old tramp is said to lurk in the woods and he might be dangerous.**'

Now think about the Hero and the Opponent Character in this story. Create a full Character Profile for these Characters as this will inspire ideas for continuation of the story.

Hero Character: Name - ....

Physical Characteristics:

Gender: ....   Age: ....   Height: ....   Build: ....

Features: (Hair) ....   (Skin) ....   (Eyes) ....

Nationality: ....   Clothing: ....

Skills/Interests: ....   Occupation: ....

Social Characteristics:

Relationships with others: ....

Attitude to others: ....

Viewed by others: ....

Psychological Characteristics:

Positive Traits: ....

Negative Traits: ....

Significant Past Event: ....

Beliefs and Attitudes: ....

Opponent Character: Name - ....

Physical Characteristics:

Gender: ....   Age: ....   Height: ....   Build: ....

Features: (Hair) ....   (Skin) ....   (Eyes) ....

Nationality: ....   Clothing: ....

Skills/Interests: ....   Occupation: ....

Social Characteristics:
Relationships with others: ....
Attitude to others: ....
Viewed by others: ....

Psychological Characteristics:
Positive Traits: ....
Negative Traits: ....
Significant Past Event: ....
Beliefs and Attitudes: ....

Relevant details from the **Three Aspects of Character** can now be added to enhance the story and develop Characters.

Example: Using **'The Sad Clown'** story, add in relevant Character details to enhance the story and reveal things about the Characters.

'Billy approaches the big top with trepidation. Where is Coco the clown? His flowing white costume, painted face and big red nose always made him feel happy. During the performance the day before he had laughed until tears of joy streamed down his cheeks; but where was Coco today?

It was the last day of the circus. Soon they would take him back to the orphanage; back to that lonely, cold room. She, Miss Dagon, would be at the door to meet him. **There would be a cruel snarl on her face and she would no doubt find an excuse to send him to bed without his tea. Billy was not sure why she treated him so badly. The other children did not seem to annoy her so much.** Billy had to find Coco first, but he would have to be quick. **Miss Dagon would be waiting. The thought hung over him like a cloud...**

To himself, he called her Miss Dragon. If she ever found out, his life would not be worth living. Ever since she had screamed at him for trampling on her precious flowers by mistake, he had hated her. That day she had told him he deserved to lose his parents; it was God's justice for being such a wicked boy.

Then she yelled, "You're just like my evil, wicked son. You even look like him, you little devil."
Billy didn't understand. As he turned away, she took out a letter, ripped it up and threw the pieces on the ground. Then she stamped on it and trampled it underfoot. One small fragment read, "I never want to see you again. You never loved me as a mother. I hate you."

Every day she pruned and tended those flowers in the orphanage yard; waddling from bloom to bloom with a silly grin on that chubby face. She only cared about the flowers. Billy knew his tea would be burnt or cold and his clothes would always hang on him like a scarecrow. She did not care if they were too big or just hand-me-downs...

Billy is still lost in his thoughts when he reaches the outside. No one had noticed **Billy's slender form** slide off the seat, make its way to the entrance and slip past the ticket barrier. Outside he sees Coco alone by the side of the Big Top with his head in his hands. **Billy feels scared** but he reaches out a friendly hand. Coco draws back.

"I'm not funny anymore," Coco blurts.

Billy considers, "I still laugh at you."
Coco continues, without hearing Billy.

"No one laughs at my pranks. They just giggle because I'm too old and pathetic to be a clown anymore."

At close quarters Billy notices the wrinkles; the haggard look on Coco's face. Even the grease paint can't hide the truth. Billy hesitates for a moment.

Then he protests, "But I love the prat falls; the jokes that don't work properly."

Billy notices there are dark stains all over Coco's beautiful blue and white striped costume. Coco lifts a can of beer unsteadily to his lips. More of it spills over Coco's chest and Billy recoils at the stench of alcohol.

Coco slurs, "That's just it, they don't work and you're just **one little kid**. What do you know?"

Billy pulls away. Coco looks up suddenly and sees Billy's eyes fill up with tears.

"Sorry, I didn't mean that."

Billy turns and runs away crying uncontrollably.

Coco looks up. A **huge**, **burly** woman stands over him.

"Have you seen a boy called Billy?"

Coco shakes his head, then gulps more beer. She lumbers away.'

Exercise 3: 7

Think about '**The Dark Forest**' story. Write about the first encounter the Hero Character has with the Tramp (Opponent).

'The trees seem to close in on me. I edge forward. Branches appear to reach out and grab me. There is no way out. Where is the path? I squint, but can only just see the watch face. Nine o'clock and it is nearly dark. I left three hours ago. Father warned me never to go into the forest because of what happened there three years ago. What did he mean? All he said was a mysterious old tramp lurks in the woods and he might be dangerous. Suddenly, a twig cracks. I can see a dark shadow passing between the trees. Someone is watching me!'

....

....

....

....

....

....

....

....

....

....

....

....

c. Active Character Description

It is essential to use **Active** rather than **Passive Description** when describing Characters. Characters are alive and living things never stop moving throughout their lives. Always describe your Characters in Movement e.g. It is better to say *'He wiped his furrowed brow'* than *'His brow was furrowed'*.

Example: Using *'The Operation'* story, demonstrate the use of Active Character Description.

'As I lie in this hospital bed I feel a sharp pain in my abdomen. I call it my tummy, but that's the word the doctor used. The pain's getting worse and I feel really scared. My mum's gone to buy some

coffee and she says she's not worried because it's not a serious illness. How would she know? I've been in and out of hospital so many times in the last few months. I feel like crying but I don't want them to think I'm a baby. Dad says, 'men don't cry'. I'm only a boy, but maybe he's right. The nurse with the shiny blonde hair says it won't hurt anymore if they take out my appendix, but I'm not so sure. Ouch! It hurts. What's really wrong with me?

I yell, "Nurse! Nurse!"'

Descriptions of the nurse Character would be dull in the Passive mode. e.g. *'She had a trim figure, slender fingers and deep blue eyes.'* Instead they are written in the Active mode (see the description as the story continues).

'She appears; her trim figure gliding to the bed. She flings back the covers and her slender fingers probe my belly. Her deep blue eyes stare momentarily, then flash with concern.

"It seems that appendix must come out Robbie."
Mum slips past the cubicle curtain clasping a piping hot coffee. Her face glows red from the cold outside. She sighs with relief.

"Dad is glad to hear you're being brave about it," she blurts contentedly, "he says you better not let him down again."
Dad always made me look stupid. As I remember my eyes smart...

He cuffed me with the boxing glove. It nearly knocked me cold. His muscles rippled as he danced skilfully round me.

"Come on you weakling, punch! I'll teach you to deal with those bullies. What's the matter with you?"

"I can't Dad, I can't. I'm scared!"
He flung his arms up in despair, dumped the gloves on the floor and marched out...

The nurse lifts the syringe and squirts some liquid. *I'm terrified!*'

Exercise 3: 8

Think about **'The Crash'** story where '*A police officer is first on the scene of a car crash*'. Describe the Characters in an Active way as you continue the story. ae

'*The wheels of the overturned van were still spinning as* **John leapt from his squad car**. *The flashing blue lights reflected in the puddles of freshly fallen rainwater.* **The van door eased open slowly and a blood soaked hand reached out. John gasped in horror.** *It was his first day. He had always wanted to be a police officer, but this was too much.*

He brushed the beads of sweat from his brow and hurried to the door. He saw the slumped form of a man trying to ease himself out from behind a crumpled steering wheel. He was mouthing something. John carefully supported the man's head. It was sticky. The grey hair was matted with blood. The man's breathing became shallow. *He needed to get help fast.*'

....

....

....

....

....

....

....

....

....

....

....

d. Identifying with a Character

The reader must be able to **Identify** emotionally with a Hero Character otherwise they will lose interest. There are three ways to create Identification with your Hero Character.

1. Put your Hero Character in Jeopardy or Danger.
This does not have to be life threatening but the Character must be in danger of losing something or facing trouble. We have shown some Characters in difficult situations in stories like *'The Tunnel'*, *'The Sad Clown'* and *'The Magic Key'*.

2. Your Hero Character is Likeable.
• The Character demonstrates they are a good person.
e.g. In *'The Inferno'* story, a fire officer shows great bravery and risks his life to rescue a child from a burning building.
• The Character is funny and amuses us.
e.g. In *'The Magic Key'* story, Hannah, the Hero Character, tells the story of her birthday party in a mildly humorous way.
• The Character is good at or very skilled at something.
e.g. In *'The Crash'* story, a police officer demonstrates the emergency skills he has learnt during his training.

3. Your Hero Character suffers some Undeserved Misfortune.
e.g. In the *'Lost'* story, Paul is separated from his mother. We feel sympathy for him because he is unfairly and unjustly treated.

4. Your Hero Character should always be Courageous.
The Character displays emotional courage in their actions.
e.g. In *'The Sad Clown'* story, Billy puts up with cruelty.

Example:  Using the *'Lost'* story, create Identification with Paul by subjecting him to undeserved misfortune and putting him in jeopardy.

We could write a tragic Memory (Flashback) for Paul. This will create a Backstory and evoke sympathy for him.

'A small boy stood on a crowded platform, clutching his mother's hand tightly. He looked up into her face. She stared blankly at the hoardings but Paul could still see the smeared eye make-up; a left-over from the tears she had shed that day. What was she thinking? He felt confused.

Paul had asked about Grandad as he had seen so many tubes and machines around him. There had been flowers by the bed and lots of cards. Grandad seemed to be sleeping. His tousled grey hair looked lank and his usually smiling face seemed contorted. All Paul could hear was a faint bleeping sound and Grandad's shallow breaths. It was scary. A man in black with a white collar had visited and said some very strange words over Grandad. Then Mummy had said Grandad would not be coming this Friday. Grandad had always bought him sweets on Fridays since Daddy left. He never shouted or got angry like Mummy did. Grandad was always kind. Paul had tugged at Grandad's arm but there was no response. Why didn't Grandad pat him on the head as usual? Mummy had pulled him away and said they had to go. What did it all mean?

The train roared from the tunnel. The screech of brakes brought it to a sudden halt. The crowds surged forward and Paul felt himself sucked into a vacuum of warm bodies, imprisoned by trouser legs and long, flowing skirts on all sides.

The train doors slid closed. Just a moment before, Paul had been holding his mother's hand. Now she was on the other side of the glass. Terror filled his mind; he had lost his mum and he might never see her again. His hand had slipped from hers as he dashed excitedly through the open doors thinking she would follow, but it was the wrong train.'

Exercise 3: 9

Think about the *'Inferno'* story where a fire officer tries to rescue a child from a burning building. Create Identification with the fire officer and the child by putting them in jeopardy.

'The flames leapt up the side of the building. Jim was scared. He had only been on shift since midnight. The screams were getting louder. He could see a fair-haired child at the window. The seconds were ticking by. He must act quickly! He knew there was so little time. The other firemen were shaking their heads saying it was too late to get her out. Jim took the hose and doused himself with water. He could feel the fire's heat and he was fifty yards away. Tiles began to cascade from the roof. Jim edged his way forward. All he could see in his mind was the desperate face of the little girl. Could he save her?'

....

....

....

....

....

....

....

....

....

....

....

4. What happens in the Story?
a. What is the Story About?

All stories can be reduced to one simple statement:
This is a story about ....Hero.... **who wants to** .The Goal of the Hero.
The story must be about the Goal of the Hero Character and the opposition they face in achieving that Goal. This could be termed as a **Single Line of Action**. Only the story content which is relevant to the desire of the hero should be included. A reader will also Identify strongly with a Hero Character who has a strong and clearly defined Goal.

Example:

Use the single statement, '**This is a story about** .... **who wants to** ....' as a way of defining what some of the stories used so far are about.

'**This is a story about**' means we must state important and relevant details about the Hero Character.
'**Who wants to**' means we state the aim or Goal of the Hero Character (Single Line of Action that will drive the story).

Example 1: The story of '**The Sad Clown**'.
This is a story about a boy called Billy, a lonely orphan **who wants to** run away from the orphanage with Coco the clown to find a better and happier life.

Example 2: The '**Lost**' story.
This is a story about a little boy called Paul. He is on his way home from seeing his sick grandad in hospital and gets lost. It is about a child **who wants to** find his mother again.

Example 3: The story of '**The Christmas Lights**'.
This is a story about a young girl from a poor home who has no siblings or friends **who wants to** see the special wish she has made of Father Christmas come true.

Exercise 3: 10

Write the Single Statement 'This is a story about .... who wants to ....' for the following stories.

'The Tunnel' story.
This is a story about ....

....

who wants to ....

....

'The Operation' story.
This is a story about ....

....

who wants to ....

....

The **'Inferno'** story.
This is a story about ....

....

who wants to ....

....

b. What Happens in the Story?

We must decide how the story develops. This is the Single Line of Action or **Plot Line** of the story. **A Narrative is just a series of Events, but a Plot Line is the way those Events are ordered.** The Hero Character will follow this Line of Action to achieve their aim or Goal. The opposition and difficulties the Hero faces will constitute the story until the aim or Goal is either achieved (happy ending) or lost (tragic ending).

According to the Greek philosopher and dramatist **Aristotle**, who lived over two and a half millennia ago, a story can be broken into three parts. It is made up of a:

Beginning • Middle • End

Most stories that work follow a straightforward structure or pattern that can be summarised as follows:

The Beginning (about one quarter of the story)

The Beginning or Set-up of a story is the most important part. You must establish a number of things in an interesting way.

• Where the story happens (three Locations is sufficient).

• When the story happens (simple references are best).

• Who is involved in the story (Hero and Opponent).

• What happens in the story - Establish the Crisis that starts the action, the Goal or aim of the Hero to put it right and the potential Conflict that is likely if this path is followed.

The Middle (about one half of the story)

• The Hero Character appears to be making good ground. There is Conflict and opposition from the Opponent but it looks like this will be overcome.

• Things become increasingly difficult. The Opponent is more successful and the level of Conflict begins to build to fever pitch. In the end it looks as if the Hero Character will be a total failure. The Hero Character will be at his wits end.

The End (about one quarter of the story)

• The climax of the story will involve a confrontation between the Hero Character and the Opponent Character. This will result in either success (happy ending) or failure (tragic ending) for the Hero Character.

• The Closing Off of the story will show the new situation for the Hero Character.

c. Planning a Story

Using the basic structure of Beginning, Middle and End it is possible to plan stories in some detail. A good plan gives direction, focus and a structured framework for the story.

Using the *'My Dog Jack'* idea, create a Story Plan with a Beginning, Middle and End.

A **Story Plan** can be created by asking these questions:

The Beginning

Where does the story happen? A dog rescue centre, a park, the veterinary practice, the home and at the dog's grave.

When does the story happen? A series of Events over a three year period.

Who are the main Characters in the story?

• **Hero Character** - Tina, a ten year old girl who is missing her real mum.

• **Opponent Character** - A stepmother with a controlling attitude who hates Tina's dog.

• **Sidekick Character** - Tina's dog Jack.

• **Other Characters** - Father, veterinary surgeon, nurse.

What Crisis starts the action? The moment Jack tears up the furniture and the stepmother says he has to go.

The Single Statement - This story is about a girl called Tina who is ten years old. Her mother has left the family home and she is now looked after by a controlling and dominant stepmother she does not like. She wants to save her dog Jack, whom she loves, from being destroyed.

The Middle

List **three Events**, connected with or caused by the Opponent, that **complicate the action**. They must get progressively worse.

1. Tina's stepmum tells her father over dinner that either the dog goes or she does. Her father is so weak he gives in.

2. A local child is attacked by a dog and Tina's stepmum lies about Jack escaping off his lead and carrying out the attack.

3. When Jack is condemned to die for the attack, Tina runs away to a local park with Jack. The police look for her and

Jack and, after a desperate chase, they find them.

The End

What is the Climax of the story? Tina's stepmum takes Jack to the vet to be destroyed. Tina protests that it is all based on a lie, but to no avail. Jack dies.

What Closes Off the story? Tina visits Jack's grave. Her stepmum arrives to take her back. When they arrive home the police are waiting for Tina's stepmum. Her father has told them she lied about the dog. As Tina's stepmum is led away, her father brings in a tiny puppy and gives it to Tina.

Exercise 3: 11

Think of *'The Tunnel'* story again. Invent a Story Plan by answering the following questions about the Beginning, Middle and End.

The Beginning

Where does the story happen? ....
....
When does the story happen? ....
....
Who are the main Characters in the story?
• Hero Character ....
• Opponent Character ....
• Sidekick Character ....
• Other Characters ....
What Crisis starts the action? ....
....
The Single Statement - This story is about ....
....
.... who wants to ....
....
....

The Middle

List three Events, connected with or caused by the Opponent, that complicate the action. They must get progressively worse.

1. ....

....

2. ....

....

3. ....

....

The End

What is the Climax of the story? ....

....

....

....

What Closes Off the story? ....

....

....

5. Why Does your Story Happen?
a. Why Write This Particular Story?

The Theme of the Story

Every story carries a message. Why have these Events happened and what is their deeper meaning or significance? This may not be clear when we first start writing but as the story develops it often emerges. Every story carries a Message which is often deep or has life-changing significance. It reflects our view on a particular subject. This is called the **Theme** or **Controlling Idea**. It can be:

An Issue - e.g. A story showing how bullying affects the victim or how animals should never be treated cruelly etc.

A Moral - e.g. Crime doesn't pay; liars are always found out; love overcomes hate; good defeats evil.

Example: | Define the Theme or Controlling Idea of some of the stories we have developed so far.

Every story does have a Theme or Controlling Idea. It can either be an Issue or a Moral. Sometimes it can be difficult to spot your Theme straight away, but once it is clear it can give the story more direction, clarity and focus.

Example 1: *'The Sad Clown'* story.
Theme - 'Being valued and loved by just one person can make everything you do in life worthwhile'.

Example 2: *'The Tunnel'* story.
Theme - This is an example where the Theme is not clear because the story needs further development. It could be: 'Being alive is more important than being rich'.

Example 3: *'The Christmas Lights'* story.
Theme - This is another example where the Theme is not yet entirely clear. If the wish is about having a new sibling then it could be: 'We all need at least one friend'.

Exercise 3: 12

Let's think again about some of the stories we have developed. Try and identify the Themes of these stories.

The *'Lost'* story.
Theme - ....
....

The *'My Dog Jack'* story.
Theme - ....
....

The *'Inferno'* story.
Theme - ....
....

The Motive or Reason for Writing

Creative Writing should always attempt to **engage the reader emotionally**. There also might be a **Theme** or **Message** the writer wishes to communicate. This Theme or Message needs to affect the reader in a particular way. Therefore the **Motive** or **Reason for Writing** could be any of the following:

Inform • Explain • Interest • Challenge • Arouse Humour • Scare • Shock • Entertain • Excite

---

Example:

| Use an extract of **'The Crash'** story to show how the writing attempts to shock the reader. |

'The wheels of the overturned van were still spinning as John leapt from his squad car. The flashing blue lights reflected in the puddles of freshly fallen rainwater. The van door eased open slowly and a blood soaked hand reached out. John gasped in horror. It was his first day. He had always wanted to be a police officer, but this was too much.'

Exercise 3: 13

Try continuing this story called **'Chase'**. Write to scare your reader.

'As I turned the corner into a dark and secluded alleyway, I heard footsteps quicken behind me. I turned round, but there was no one there. I made off again, winding left into an even more narrow passage; a sharp distinct scuffling made me stop again. I listened; only silence. I peered into the darkness; a tall, ominous shadow loomed across the path. Would I ever get home?'

....

....

....

....

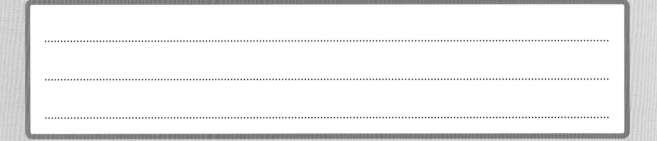

The Choice of Genre

Once we have decided why we are writing a particular story we must choose a **Genre**. This just means type or category of writing. Every genre creates a specific emotional expectation in the reader. There are three general categories of writing:

- **Fiction** (made up) or **Non-fiction** (based on real Events)
- **Autobiographical** (based on Events in our own life)
- **Biographical** (based on Events in another person's life)

The above material can be found in many **Story Types**. These Story Types have certain elements. A detailed study of Genre is not possible here, but here are some common Story Types:

Adventure • Detective • Myths • Fairy Story • Horror
Murder/Mystery • Love Story • Science Fiction

These Story Types can be delivered in a number of ways:

Journals • Diaries • Interviews • Dialogue • Narrative
Speeches • Ballads • Travelogues • Reports • Poems

The Style of Writing

This is linked to our purpose for writing. If we wish the story to have a particular effect then the style of language and tone of the writing is of great importance. Writing can be:

Argumentative • Satirical (ridiculing something)
Comic • Reflective or Thoughtful • Sympathetic
Serious • Descriptive • Tragic • Persuasive
Discursive (discussing a topic) • Racy • Critical

The Target Audience

The story can be written for children or adults or both.

Using the *'Little Red Riding Hood'* story, write as if you are the young girl. Write it in the Narrative Form in a serious style. Target the story for children.

The fairy story Genre has magical elements and it often contains a Moral for young children. e.g. Little Red Riding Hood is about not talking to strangers or taking risks. The Narrative Form is the most common form of storytelling.

'As I left the small cottage with my basket, Mother was still calling out, "Don't talk to strangers, do you hear?"

I pulled the bright red hood hard down over my ears so as not to listen. Mother did go on and on sometimes. I turned into the woods. It shouldn't take too long to get to Grandma's house and I was sure she would like the fruit in the basket.

The path wound round and the forest became darker and denser. Suddenly a huge wolf stepped out from the bushes...'

Exercise 3: 14 Try continuing this diary entry by a child who takes a ride on *'The Ghost Train'*.

'Friday: My day at the fair was very unusual. It all started when I boarded the ghost train. We trundled into the tunnel...'

....

....

....

....

....

....

....

....

b. Why Does your Hero Character Act in this Way?

Every Hero Character should have a clear **Goal** or Single Line of Action. This can be understood as their **Outward Motivation**. This is what the Character outwardly wants.

For example in the *'Lost'* story we could say:
This is a story about a little boy called Paul, who gets lost on his way home from seeing his sick grandad in hospital. **He wants to** find his mother again.

We can now go on to ask - **why does he want this**?
This is something that comes from within and we can call this the **Inward Motivation. This is always related to the lack of Self-worth or Self-esteem of the person.**
Everybody wants to feel better about themselves, to grow, develop and improve their lot in life. However, we may not always make the right choices that aid us in this lifetime quest.

In the *'Lost'* story, Paul will want to find his mother again because, without her, he will feel lost and lonely. He will not be able to grow into the young man he ought to be, without the proper nurture and support his mother can give him.

Example: Using *'The Dark Forest'* story, show why the Hero Character might act in a particular way.

This story is about a very talented, self-important boy.
Outward Motivation - He wants to become a great musician as he believes this will bring him fame, fortune and celebrity.
Inward Motivation - He needs to constantly show people how good he is at everything, which suggests he may not feel as good on the inside as he should.

'As I leave the rehearsal, I congratulate myself on another successful day. Again the music master has said I have the talent

to become a professional cellist some day. Mozart was a child protégé and maybe I am too. I feel on top of the world and nothing is too hard for me. I have been asked to play a solo at the end of year school concert. It is a great honour and all the local diginitaries will be there. The headteacher has invited the principal of the Royal Academy of Music to hear me. It's so exciting. I will be playing the two most famous cello pieces in the repertoire: 'The Swan' by Saint Saens and the Elgar 'Cello Concerto'. I can't wait. Everybody will applaud and I will be the centre of attention. One day 'Paul Langdon' will be a household name.

It's late and the rehearsal went on and on because the rest of the orchestra were slow at picking things up. Darkness closes in outside the school. My father gets very worried about me these days. I walk briskly out of the school gates and down the country lane. I pass by way of the forest. There is a forest path I could take that would get me home much quicker.

However, this is where Jake was last seen. A twin brother, but so different from me. We played together when we were really small but I could always out smart him. They said he was a bit dim at school; reading was a problem and his spelling; well that was atrocious. I was his protector at school. He was always at the bottom of the class and I was always at the top of the class. We were like chalk and cheese, to use a cliché. I couldn't understand why he seemed so stupid. We came from the same family. I still miss him though; since Jake went missing nothing has ever been the same. When you are a twin it's like a part of you is gone; your arm has been cut off or something.

Dad says I must be home by seven, whatever happens. I hesitate; what about this forest route? It's the fastest way, but no one goes there anymore since Jake disappeared...

The blue lights flashed continually from stationary police cars surrounding the forest. Searchlights from the circling helicopters probed the thick, leafy canopy of the trees. My father had never quite recovered from the death of my mother and now he had to cope with a missing son. For weeks they had combed the forest but nothing was ever found. Jake had vanished into thin air. He was supposed to stay at school for an extra reading class but he never came home. Where was he?...

What if I disappear like Jake? It's a difficult choice. No, that will never happen to me. Anyway, if I take the long way round and get home late, I'll get into big trouble with Dad. If I take the forest path and get home in half the time, everything will be fine. No one will ever know that I went into the 'dark forest', as everyone now calls it. I just won't tell them. It will only take twenty minutes. I will run as fast as I can before night falls. If I don't move quickly, every part of the forest will be shrouded in shadows and darkness and it will be really scary.

The decision is made: in I go. The path is clear and there is no problem following it. I feel really good; it will take even less time than I think. Why didn't I take this route before? The ferns and bracken appear to part before me. The dirt track is clearly visible every step of the way. It twists and turns a little but it is so obvious. How could anybody ever get lost? If Jake got lost I don't know how. It just confirms to me how stupid he must have been. What a thought to have about someone who went missing; particularly your own twin brother.

Suddenly, the path runs out. I turn round and attempt to go back but there appears to be no path. The night closes in. What's happening? All that certainty evaporates and I know I'm lost.

I dash to the right and there are only bushes and thorn briars. What about the left? Again there is no path; it can't be! I cut my legs on the branches. I panic; what am I to do? Is this what Jake felt three years ago in this forest? What if I meet the legendary inhabitant of the forest?

I'm so scared. All my plans of future fame and fortune seem a distant memory now. I may never leave this forest; I may disappear like Jake and never be found again. I wish I'd listened to my dad. How stupid I've been.'

Exercise 3: 15

Invent some Inward Motivations for the following Hero Characters.

Remember: Inward Motivation in a Character always relates in some way to a lack of Self-worth or Self-esteem.

1. 'The Ghost Train'
Outward Motivation - The Character wants to try out all the most dangerous and scary rides at the funfair.
Inward Motivation - *She wants to prove to her friends she is not a coward. Her mother and father never let her take risks.*

2. 'The Chase'
Outward Motivation - The Character wants to get home in a hurry and decides to take a short cut everybody says is dangerous.

Inward Motivation - ....

....

3. 'Little Red Riding Hood'
Outward Motivation - The girl is told by her mother she must take some supplies to Grandma. She tends to disobey her mother.

Inward Motivation - ....

....

Your Own Story - Draft One

This is your chance to write your own story using one of the following scenarios as a starting point.

On the next page are two story scenarios. Choose either:

Story 3 - *'The Toy Room'* or

Story 4 - *'The Secret Attic'*

• Use the learning points in this chapter to help you write.

• Observe the basic rules below to help structure your story.

• Write **Story 3** or **4** in this book. Once you have learnt the principles, you can write the other story on separate sheets of paper.

The Five Elements of Story

Try and include ideas and techniques from this chapter.

1. Where? - A mansion with a toy room/bedroom containing puppets, tin soldiers, teddy bears, rag or china dolls, a doll's house, clockwork toys or a mansion with a secret attic room that contains old theatrical costumes, stage props and a mysterious old chest.

2. When? - Victorian era, Christmas Eve, night-time.

3. Who? - Child (Hero), stepmother, mother, aunt or toys (Opponent). A Flashback Memory could provide more Characters.

4. What? - The toys or props could magically come to life; this could be imaginary or a child will discover something in an old chest. A big confrontation with the Opponent Character could happen during either story.

5. Why? - Give your story a Theme.

Observe these Rules and complete the Story

1. The Character is not allowed to leave the space. You must find a way to end the story in the space without leaving it.

2. One other Character can enter the space and leave the space at some point in the story.

3. Write out the scenario first and then continue the story.

 ae

First Draft - Story 3

'The Toy Room'

Opening Scenario in Past Tense:

'The door slammed. It echoed through the corridors of the old mansion. A key turned in the lock. Anger raged inside ...Name... *as he/she bit back the tears. He/she ran to the door and tried it. It was no use.*

...Name... *yelled, "You never let me stay up. I hate you!"*
He/she heard footsteps move away from the door. ...Name... *slumped on the bed for a few moments. The candle guttered. The room was growing dark.* ...Name... *heard noises outside, jumped off the bed and snatched up Teddy. He/she slipped past the rocking horse and over to the window. It was Christmas Eve. In the dim light* ...Name... *could see children were playing outside in the snow.* ...Name... *clutched Teddy tightly.'*

First Draft - Story 4

'The Secret Attic'

Opening Scenario in Past Tense:

' ...Name... *closed the door behind him/her.* ...Name... *had escaped. Auntie had said that the mysterious attic room at the top of the old mansion was strictly off limits, but* ...Name... *had finally entered it. He/she turned the key in the lock. Now he/she felt really safe, even if the room was a bit creepy.* ...Name... *couldn't be punished if he/she could not be found. The room was lit by a thin shaft of moonlight coming from a tiny roof light. There were rows of old costumes on hangers. Theatre props littered the room: old swords, pistols, clubs, fans, faded black and white photographs of actors, walking sticks and umbrellas. Then* ...Name... *saw it; a large wooden chest in the middle of the room. It seemed to beckon him/her forward.* ...Name... *carefully eased back the lid. As the dust cloud settled,* ...Name... *eyes widened at what he/she saw. Suddenly there was a noise...'*

Choose to write either **Story 3** or **Story 4**, then use the Planning page to write down some ideas for your story.

Planning - 1st Draft
Story 3
'The Toy Room'

....

....

....

....

....

....

....

....

....

....

....

....

....

....

....

....

....

If you have chosen **Story 3 - 'The Toy Room'**, copy out the opening scenario on Story Page 1 - 1st Draft, then continue your story on the pages that follow.

Planning - 1st Draft
Story 4
'The Secret Attic'

Let's write a new story.

....

....

....

....

....

....

....

....

....

....

....

....

....

....

....

....

....

....

....

If you have chosen **Story 4** - **'The Secret Attic'**, copy out the opening scenario on Story Page 1 - 1st Draft, then continue your story on the pages that follow.

Story Page 1 - 1st Draft
'The Toy Room' or 'The Secret Attic'

....

....

....

....

....

....

....

....

....

....

....

....

....

....

....

....

....

....

Story Page 2 - 1st Draft
'The Toy Room' or 'The Secret Attic'

Story Page 3 - 1st Draft
'The Toy Room' or 'The Secret Attic'

Story Page 4 - 1st Draft
'The Toy Room' or 'The Secret Attic'

Story Page 5 - 1st Draft
'The Toy Room' or *'The Secret Attic'*

....

....

....

....

....

....

....

....

....

....

....

....

....

....

....

....

....

....

'The Toy Room' or *'The Secret Attic'*

Story Page 6 - 1st Draft
'The Toy Room' or 'The Secret Attic'

....

....

....

....

....

....

....

....

....

....

....

....

....

....

....

....

....

....

....

Scores Out of Ten	Spelling & Grammar	→		Creativity	→	

'The Toy Room' or 'The Secret Attic'

Chapter Four
Story Dialogue

Dialogue is very important in stories because conversing is the main way in which Characters interact. The Conflicts and Tensions between Characters are mostly expressed through Dialogue. Dialogue can also give your reader very important insights about the motives of your main Characters.

Indirect Speech • Direct Speech
Direct Speech Introductions • Speech Patterns
Revealing Character • Using Second Person

1. Indirect (Reported) Speech

Indirect or **Reported Speech** is a very important device for telling stories. **It occurs when the meaning of what someone said or wrote is conveyed or put across without using the exact words.** i.e. Someone is telling us what somebody else said or wrote but they are not using the actual words that were said. For example:

The girls said they were sorry for being late for tea.

This sentence conveys the meaning but the not the exact words.
No speech marks are used.
The exact words may have been:

"We're sorry we're late for tea." (Speech marks are used.)

Example: | Demonstrate the effective use of Indirect Speech in *'The Operation'* story.

'The Operation' story has now been given an opening that reveals why Robbie may have ended up in hospital. Indirect Speech is used as a tool to help fill in background details. The Indirect Speech is highlighted in Bold Typeface.

'It's 1.00pm and nearly time for lunch. Other children file past and line up for the daily choice. As usual I'm alone on my table; a packed lunch in front of me. It's been hard in this new school. Nobody talks to me. It's my first day back for a week. I can't pretend I'm sick anymore. **My mum said I have to attend now otherwise Dad will get really angry and I know what that means.** No one listens to me, not even the teachers. **They say I imagine things.** Well I'm not imagining being on my own on this table and the fact that not a single child has spoken to me since form registration.

Only one person has taken a real interest in me and that's Eric, the class bully. He, the one with the big mouth, is responsible for this situation. He's bigger than everybody else and likes throwing his weight around. **Eric told them all not to talk to me, so nobody does.** Just because I answered a question in maths that he couldn't answer; that was my first day and everybody laughed at him. I didn't know it would lead to this.

It's been three weeks and they all still ignore me. Only Patsie, the small mousy-haired girl with laughing blue eyes, tried to talk to me. **He told her she would be beaten up** so now she's backed off too. The chattering noise in the dinner hall makes my isolation even more painful. Children move towards my table because there's plenty of space and then when they see me they steer away to another table. It's just not fair.

The day wears on. Back in the classroom; it's English and then we get to do some drawing. I go to the reading shelf to select a book and then it happens. I double up and collapse in pain. Clutching my stomach, I can hardly breathe. What's happening?

Adults surround me and I hear an ambulance siren. Patsie leans over me and grips my arm reassuringly. She is quickly pushed aside by Eric. **I hear some school teachers express their concern.**

I notice Eric smirking as I am carried out an a stretcher.
    "Faking it again," I hear him quip as I pass through the doorway. I feel a surge of anger and try to lift my head to protest, but I am too weak and fall back limply on the stretcher.'

Exercise 4: 1

Think about **'The Toy Room'** or **'The Secret Attic'** story again. Rewrite a short section of the story. Include Indirect Speech to help tell the story.

....

....

....

....

....

....

....

....

....

....

....

2. Direct Speech

Direct Speech allows the story writer to give the exact words of the Character. Conversations between Characters should always be conflictual as this will retain Tension in the story.

There are **six rules** for using Direct Speech:
1. Opening or closing comments should be separated from speech with a comma.
2. Use speech marks to open and close speech.
3. Always commence speech with a capital letter.
4. If there is a break in speech but the same speaker then continues speaking and there is no full stop, no capital letter is used.
5. A new line is used for every new speaker.
6. Indent the first line of speech as if it is a new paragraph. This example shows all six rules in operation.

> *"When are we going out to the restaurant?" Peter questioned, "because I am beginning to feel very hungry."*
>
> *"Please be patient," his mum responded, "your dad will be home soon and then we can leave."*

Dos and Don'ts in Direct Speech

1. Avoid too much speech - The worst kind of stories involve pages and pages of speech. A story is not a play, so the 'talking heads' scenario should be avoided. Stories are mainly narration and speech should be included where it helps develop the story. i.e. where someone says something that is important.

e.g. a Character might say, *"I'm telling you the truth, why don't you listen to me?"* etc.

2. Always use Conflict in Direct Speech - If there is no Conflict there is no Tension and this will lose the reader.

e.g. *Martha insisted, "This is the right path, I know it."*

> *"Just like last time. You always get us lost," Tom quipped.*

Demonstrate the effective use of Direct Speech in *'The Operation'* story.

The story is now given a dramatic Event to kickstart the story. Direct Speech is highlighted in bold.

'As I lie in this hospital bed, I feel a sharp pain in my abdomen. I call it my tummy, but that's the word the doctor used. The pain's getting worse and I feel really scared.

My mum's gone to buy some coffee and she says she's not worried because it's not a serious illness. How would she know? I feel like crying, but I don't want them to think I'm a baby. Dad says, 'men don't cry'. I'm only a boy, but maybe he's right. The nurse with the shiny blonde hair says it won't hurt anymore if they take out my appendix, but I'm not so sure. Ouch! It's really painful.

I yell, "Nurse! Nurse!"

She appears; her trim figure gliding to the bed. She flings back the covers and her slender fingers probe my belly. Her deep blue eyes stare momentarily, then flash with concern.

"It seems that appendix must come out Robbie."

Mum slips past the cubicle curtain clasping a piping hot coffee. Her face glows red from the cold outside. She sighs with relief.

"Dad is glad to hear you're being brave about it," she blurts contentedly, "he says you better not let him down again."

Dad always made me look stupid. As I remember my eyes smart...

He cuffed me with the boxing glove. It nearly knocked me cold. His muscles rippled as he danced skilfully round me.

"Come on you weakling, punch! I'll teach you to deal with those bullies. What's the matter with you?"

"I can't Dad, I can't. I'm scared!"

He flung his arms up in despair, dumped the gloves on the floor and marched out...

I become aware of the room again. I feel really scared. I'm going to cry. I just can't help it. It just comes from nowhere. The tears begin to fall onto my cheeks and the bedclothes.'

Exercise 4: 2

Think about **'The Toy Room'** or **'The Secret Attic'** story again. Re-work a short section of the story and practise using Direct Speech.

....

....

....

....

....

....

....

....

....

....

....

....

....

....

3. Direct Speech Introductions

Direct Speech can be introduced by using a verb or descriptive statement before or after the speech to indicate the way the speaker delivers the line. Sometimes no introduction is needed if the line's meaning is clear and we know who is speaking.

Try to use verbs other than *'said'* or *'says'*. They are overused so use them sparingly. Here is a list of more interesting verbs: *advised; announced; answered; argued; asked; bellowed; boasted; called; continued; declared; demanded; enquired; exclaimed; gabbled; growled; joked; lied; moaned; ordered; pleaded; repeated; replied; shouted; sobbed; spoke; screamed; stammered; stuttered; suggested; warned; whispered; yelled.*

Example:  Use **'The Operation'** story to indicate effective ways of introducing Direct Speech.

'Dad's muscles rippled as he danced skilfully round me.

"Come on!" **he screamed**, *"punch! I'll teach you to deal with those bullies."*

I stammered, *"I can't Dad, I can't. I'm scared!"*

"You little weakling, what's the matter with you?"'

Exercise 4: 3 Using **'The Toy Room'** or **'The Secret Attic'** story, rewrite a section of Direct Speech using different forms of introduction.

....

....

....

....

....

4. Speech Patterns

Two important things about the way people speak:

1. Contractions in Speech:

Most people use contractions in Speech because it is quicker to say. Occasionally a person might say something in full to make more impact or emphasise what they are saying. For example, instead of saying in full: *"You are going to listen to me because I am your father,"* they will probably say *"You're going to listen to me because I'm your father."*

2. Styles of Speech:

There are many stylistic things you can do in Speech to show how your Characters talk. This will indicate the kind of people they are: age, status, background, attitude etc.

Formal and Educated Speech

e.g. *"Good evening, ladies and gentlemen. I wish to express my thanks to all our special guests at our meeting tonight."*

Informal and Uneducated Speech

e.g. *"Come 'ere you, d'yer fink I'd let you get away wiv it."*

Foreign styles of Speech

e.g. *"I not speaking English, me not understand you well."*

Impediments in Speech

e.g. *"D..d...d..d do you have the next b...b..b book?"*

Childlike Speech

e.g. *"Daddy, can you help me please with my homework? Please, please, please, I'll be a very good girl all day."*

Clipped and Economical Speech

e.g. *"No, that's enough!"* A long silence followed.

Verbose and Long-winded Speech

e.g. *"I would like to begin this austere and grand occasion by speaking in great length about and thanking heartily our most honoured and revered guest tonight."*

There are many more ways you can formulate Speech. As you develop your Characters, the way they speak in your stories will also develop. Try to imagine them speaking or base their Speech Patterns on people that you know or have met.

Example: Demonstrate the effective use of a variety of Speech Patterns in *'The Operation'* story.

The story is now given a major Crisis Event that will take the story in a new direction. Characters in this story have a variety of Speech Patterns and Direct Speech has been highlighted in bold to make it easy to spot.

'*Suddenly the door is flung open. It's my dad. He shakes his head.*

"That's enough do you 'ear. You're embarassing yerself. No son of my mine should act like a baby. Pull yerself together!"

My mother reaches forward.

"Hey son, it's alright, you're going to be okay. Don't be so hard on him Carl. He's only a child."

My dad raises a hand. His voice blurs in a tirade of high pitched curses. I have seen it all before. Then his voice booms out in a final challenge.

"When I want yer opinion, I'll ask for it, do you 'ear?"

I feel sick, my eyes close and I drift off...

...The door slammed. He was drunk again. His slurred voice pierced the darkness. I lay on my bed hoping he would not burst through the door.

"I hate you," my mum screamed.

I heard the thud and a cry of pain. Another crash and the tinkle of glass; then silence. Shaky footsteps padded up the stairs. There was a pause and I froze with fear. Suddenly the door crashed open. Before I knew it, I was wrenched from the bed. He dragged me downstairs and into the kitchen. My mother sat in a huddle on a chair. Blood streamed from the cut under her bruised eye.

"Mum," I cried. I turned and faced my dad, "You big fat beast!"

Suddenly, I found myself flying through the air. I landed against the table. Everything blurred...

...I come round again. Mother sits silent, as she always does when Dad says things.

"Now, one day son, yer goin' to stop being like your movver and yer goin' to see that bein' a real man like yer dad is what's right. The operation's nuffink; be over in no time. Take the pain like a man."

The nurse glides back into the room. She lifts the syringe and squirts some liquid. I'm terrified!

The nurse pauses. She sees my eyes flash with fear.

"Now Robbie, there's nothing to be afraid of."

Her warm reassuring smile has a magical effect. I nod and brace myself as the needle finds its mark.'

Exercise 4: 4

Think about **'The Toy Room'** or **'The Secret Attic'** story again. Rewrite a section of the story to indicate your Characters have varying Speech Patterns.

....

....

....

....

....

....

....

....

....

....

....

....

....

....

5. Revealing Character

The things people say and how they are said reveal important things about a person's character and what motivates them. **Supertext** is the actual words a person says. e.g. *"I am hungry."* **Subtext** is the hidden meaning behind the words. e.g. *"You have not fed me at all today."* This is not said but might be implied in the tone of voice, the look in someone's eye or a gesture. It is important in your writing to describe the hidden thoughts and motivations of your characters.

It is best to make your Characters conceal things from each other. This creates interest for the reader and sources of real and potential conflict.

For example if someone says, *"I like you"*, it could mean that person actually hates you but does not want you to know it. The person might be saying they like you because they want to manipulate, use or get something from you.

A double meaning in the text is called **Irony**. This can be used to create very strong emotional reactions in a reader, ranging from Anger on the one hand to Humour on the other.

Humour can be created by revealing thoughts to the reader that contrast strongly with what is being said by the speaker:

> *'Martha declared, "Wow, what a cracking outfit." She thought to herself, it didn't even fit. Paula has no style.*
>
> *"I'm so glad you like it," chirps Paula. "I chose it especially for your birthday party."*
>
> *Martha hesitated. My God, did she really think she could come here in that heap of rags?*
>
> *She smiles wryly, "Oh, that's so sweet, how thoughtful."'*

Anger can be created in the reader by showing the Character is acting with deceit and has nasty or evil intentions.

> *'Dina invited her new friend Elizabeth into her bedroom.*
>
> *"Do you like it? I chose the wallpaper myself."*
>
> *Elizabeth sat on the bed and furtively eyed the large CD collection. She felt envious. It wasn't fair she thought to herself. Dina had all she wanted. Her parents were rich.*
>
> *Elizabeth smiled, "It's wonderful."*
>
> *"And the posters; what do you think?"*
>
> *Dina stood up suddenly and left the room.*
>
> *"Where are you going?" quizzed Elizabeth.*
>
> *"I'm getting my new best friend a drink of orange."*

Elizabeth went over to the CD collection and fingered the covers.
Then she slipped two of the CDs into her bag. She heard the clink of
glass from downstairs.

    Elizabeth yelled, "You're so clever."

    "What did you say? I can't hear. Just coming!"

A knowing smile crossed Elizabeth's face. She held the bag tightly as
Dina entered holding tumblers, filled to the brim.'

Example: Demonstrate how the way Characters speak can indicate character traits in **'The Operation'** story.

The Operation story now moves to its Midpoint (another Crisis Event that will take the story in a new direction). The Characters in the story do not reveal all their thoughts through what they say. However, clues are given about their motives: **Carl (the father)** acts tough and says he wants his son to be tough. Actually he is a bully and a coward and tries to conceal what he has really done to Robbie by what he says. **Robbie (the son)** tries not to show he is afraid of having the operation, because he does not want to displease his father. Eventually he confronts how he really feels and says it. He is actually far braver than his father but doesn't know it yet. **Jenny (the mother)** has not faced up to the fact that Carl is abusive and violent. She makes excuses for him and this has led to her son being seriously injured by her husband.

Direct Speech has been highlighted in bold to enable close inspection of the relevant passages. Look for the subtext or hidden meanings behind what the Characters are saying.

'I awake and there are voices echoing around me. The lights above
are a blue haze. As I try to move, there is a sudden stab of pain in
my abdomen. I manage to lift my chest a little.

I tilt my head, but vision blurs. The dreamy view betrays the same puny frame; thin pale arms and sunken chest. I think; I'll never be like my dad. More thoughts swim around my head; the operation, has it happened? Surely I'm still waiting to go to surgery? Where's the nurse?

My vision clears. I see a large pad and plasters covering my belly. What's going on? I try to move again but a searing, burning fire rushes through me. I drop back senseless. Then the voices become clear.

"Son, don't move, you're all bandaged up."

I turn my head to see Dad by the bed and Mum sits just behind him. His shaved head glistens under the white lights. A muscular arm reaches across; the tattooed anchor and 'I love yer Jenny' clearly shows. His huge hand pats my arm.

"Now you take it easy boy. You've been in the wars."

At that moment the door clicks open and the nurse with blue eyes slips through. She is followed by a bearded man in a long white coat with a stethoscope slung loosely round his neck.

My dad pulls back and draws himself up to his full height. He towers over the small wiry frame of the consultant, in his short white coat.

"Hi doc, when's the boy up and out? Nothing keeps Carl's son in the woods."

The doctor ignores the comment and takes my pulse. The nurse hovers nervously near the bed.

"Right Mr Edwards, I think we need a word. I'm afraid things are not as we thought. Robbie does not have anything wrong with his appendix."

"*Yeah, nothin' wrong as I thought. It's all in his imagination as usual.*"

My mum prods him lightly.

"*Carl, he wouldn't make it up.*"

"*Hey, hands off! He's been scared to go to school for six weeks. I'm fed up with all these games.*"

I feel terrible again. The bickering goes on and on. My head begins to spin and beads of sweat ooze from my forehead. I am too weak even to brush them away. I close my eyes to block it all out. I feel so tired and everything seems like a dream. Then suddenly I become aware there is shouting again, but I keep my eyes closed.

"*The doctor yells, "Stop it!"*"

There is silence.

"*Don't you tell me what to do. I'll sort you out.*'"

Exercise 4: 5

Think about **'The Toy Room'** or **'The Secret Attic'** story again. Rewrite a section of the story to show how dialogue can reveal character traits.

....

....

....

....

....

....

....

....

....

....

....

....

6. Using the Second Person

The **Second Person** refers to the use of the pronoun *'you'* or *'your'*. It is aptly named the Accusative case since, when it is used, it feels as if a person is being accused of something.

It cannot be used for narrating a story but it is an effective device in dialogue. If one Character continually says *'you this'* or *'you that'* to another Character, it feels like a personal attack and will soon lead to arguments and Conflict.

Example: | Using **'The Operation'** story, show how the use of the Second Person can help create Conflict.

We rejoin the story as Carl continues his angry outburst towards Robbie's doctor. Notice how the use of the word *'you'* helps build the level of Conflict between the Characters.

> *"You doctors are all the same. Yer fink yer know everyfink don't yer?"*
>
> *The consultant stammers, "Mr Edwards, you are not being reasonable."*
>
> *"Oh no, well I know what your game is. Tryin' to blame me ain't yer!"*
>
> *My mum tries to calm the situation.*
>
> *"Now Carl, the doctor's just trying to help Robbie."*
>
> *"Shut up, you! You 'ear?"*

The doctor raises his voice.

"How dare you behave in this way in here."

Something falls over and there is a loud crash.

"Now look what you've done. This is expensive equipment."

My dad's voice goes into that high pitched yell, "Right, I'll teach you!"

"Just like you taught Robbie; is that right Mr Edwards?" the doctor accuses, "You're nothing but a coward and a bully."

"Yeah! Now you'll get some of my medicine."

"Stop it! Stop it!" my mum yells.'

Exercise 4: 6

Think about **'The Toy Room'** or **'The Secret Attic'** story again. Rewrite a section of the Dialogue using the Second Person to build the Conflict.

....

....

....

....

....

....

....

....

....

....

....

Your Own Story - Draft Two

This is your chance to write your own story using one of the following scenarios as a starting point.

On the next page are two story scenarios. Choose either:

Story 3 - *'The Toy Room'* or

Story 4 - *'The Secret Attic'*

- Use the learning points in this chapter to help you write.
- Observe the basic rules below to help structure your story.
- Write **Story 3** or **4** in this book. Once you have learnt the principles, you can write the other story on separate sheets of paper.

Story Dialogue

1. Indirect Speech - This is when a Character or the writer of the story reports what another Character says. The meaning of the words is conveyed without using the exact words.

2. Direct Speech - This is where the exact words of the speaker are quoted. This is often used to relay conversations.

3. Direct Speech Introductions - Direct Speech is usually with a verb or statement.

4. Speech Patterns - The manner in which Characters speak in your story tells people a great deal about the Characters.

5. Revealing Character - Characters in a story rarely say what they really mean. Their words hide their real feelings.

6. Using Second Person - The constant use of 'you' in a speech makes it seems as if the person is making an accusation.

Observe these Rules and complete the Story

1. The Character is not allowed to leave the space. You must find a way to end the story in the space without leaving it.
2. One other Character can enter the space and leave the space at some point in the story.
3. Write out the scenario first and then continue the story.

Second Draft - Story 3

'The Toy Room'

Opening Scenario in Present Tense:

'*The door slams. It echoes through the corridors of the old mansion. A key turns in the lock. Anger rages inside ...Name... as he/she bites back the tears. He/she runs to the door and tries it. It is no use.*

...Name... yells, "You never let me stay up. I hate you!" He/she hears footsteps move away from the door. ...Name... slumps on the bed for a few moments. The candle gutters. The room is growing dark. ...Name... hears noises outside, jumps off the bed and snatches up Teddy. He/she slips past the rocking horse and over to the window. It is Christmas Eve. In the dim light ...Name... can see children are playing outside in the snow. ...Name... clutches Teddy tightly.'

Second Draft - Story 4

'The Secret Attic'

Opening Scenario in Present Tense:

'*...Name... closes the door behind him/her. ...Name... has escaped. Auntie said that the mysterious attic room at the top of the old mansion was strictly off limits, but ...Name... has finally entered it. He/she turns the key in the lock. Now he/she feels really safe, even if the room is a bit creepy. ...Name... can't be punished if he/she can't be found. The room is lit by a thin shaft of moonlight coming from a tiny roof light. There are rows of old costumes on hangers. Theatre props litter the room; old swords, pistols, clubs, fans, faded black and white photographs of actors, walking sticks and umbrellas. Then ...Name... sees it; a large wooden chest in the middle of the room. It seems to beckon him/her forward. ...Name... carefully eases back the lid. As the dust cloud settles, ...Name... eyes widen at what he/she sees. Suddenly there is a noise...*'

Choose to write either **Story 3** or **Story 4**, then use the Planning page to write down some ideas for your story.

Planning - 2nd Draft
Story 3
'The Toy Room'

Let's plan a second draft.

....

....

....

....

....

....

....

....

....

....

....

....

....

....

....

....

If you chose **Story 3** - **'The Toy Room'**, copy out the opening scenario on Story Page 1 - 2nd Draft, then continue your story on the pages that follow.

Planning - 2nd Draft
Story 4
'The Secret Attic'

It's time to plan a second draft.

....

....

....

....

....

....

....

....

....

....

....

....

....

....

....

....

If you chose **Story 4 - *'The Secret Attic'***, copy out the opening scenario on Story Page 1 - 2nd Draft, then continue your story on the pages that follow.

Story Page 1 - 2nd Draft
'The Toy Room' or *'The Secret Attic'*

....

....

....

....

....

....

....

....

....

....

....

....

....

....

....

....

....

....

'The Toy Room' or *'The Secret Attic'*

Story Page 2 - 2nd Draft
'The Toy Room' or 'The Secret Attic'

....

....

....

....

....

....

....

....

....

....

....

....

....

....

....

....

....

....

'The Toy Room' or 'The Secret Attic'

Story Page 3 - 2nd Draft
'The Toy Room' or 'The Secret Attic'

....

....

....

....

....

....

....

....

....

....

....

....

....

....

....

....

....

....

....

....

'The Toy Room' or **'The Secret Attic'**

Story Page 4 - 2nd Draft
'The Toy Room' or *'The Secret Attic'*

....

....

....

....

....

....

....

....

....

....

....

....

....

....

....

....

....

....

....

....

....

Story Page 5 - 2nd Draft
'The Toy Room' or 'The Secret Attic'

....

....

....

....

....

....

....

....

....

....

....

....

....

....

....

....

....

....

....

....

Story Page 6 - 2nd Draft
'The Toy Room' or *'The Secret Attic'*

....

....

....

....

....

....

....

....

....

....

....

....

....

....

....

....

....

....

Scores Out of Ten	Spelling & Grammar →		Creativity →	

Marking the Stories

If you are working with a teacher, tutor or an experienced adult the stories can be given a Creativity and a Spelling & Grammar mark.

Mark Scheme (marks 1 to 10)

Outstanding	**10 marks**	*Acceptable*	**5 marks**
Excellent	**9 marks**	*Needs some work*	**4 marks**
Very Good	**8 marks**	*Needs a lot of work*	**3 marks**
Good	**7 marks**	*Requires more effort*	**2 marks**
Satisfactory	**6 marks**	*Rework it completely*	**1 mark**

A mark below **5** means the story should be attempted again.

	Spelling & Grammar	Creativity
Story 3 - 'The Toy Room' First Draft	☐	☐
Story 4 - 'The Secret Attic' First Draft	☐	☐
Story 3 - 'The Toy Room' Second Draft	☐	☐
Story 4 - 'The Secret Attic' Second Draft	☐	☐

Total Score ☐ **+** **Total Score** ☐

Average Score
out of 10
(Divide total by 8)

☐

Overall Percentage

☐ %

Total Score

☐

CERTIFICATE OF

ACHIEVEMENT

This certifies

_____

has successfully completed

11+ Creative Writing

WORKBOOK **2**

Overall percentage
score achieved

%

Comment _____

_____

Signed _____
(teacher/parent/guardian)

Date _____